by

Andrew Newbound

Illustrated by Dan Chernett

For Alex, Nathan and Zara

With special thanks to:

Alaa
Amina
Daisy Attlee
Brigida Vani
Cameron Carr
Lewis Coates
Elliot Eagleton
James Eggins
Daniel Fairchild
Claire Ford
Curtis Gerrish
Taylor Hepworth
Khalid

Mahdi
Mira
Naila
Oniks
Jake Pearce
Liam Pender
Tiffany Ramsey
Reshma Rahman
Rizwana Rahman
Tafari
Rebecca Thomas
Morgan Williams
Carissa Young

First published in 2011 in Great Britain by
Barrington Stoke Ltd
18 Walker St, Edinburgh, EH3 7LP

www.barringtonstoke.co.uk

ISBN: 978-1-84299-942-4

Printed in China by Leo

Contents

Chapter 1
Finn Grabs the Gadgets

Finn Rock closed the shed door and tipped out all the stuff from his dad's work bag onto a bench. He picked up a file that said "MI6 – Top Secret". It was a list of the things on the bench:

Secret Springs for both feet

2 Blue-tooth earplugs

1 Hackberry phone – adapted for the army

6 electro-magnets made to look like coins

Finn loved it when his dad, Stan Rock, came home with work stuff. Stan tested gadgets for MI6, the government spy service. It was his job to make sure each gadget worked before the spies used it for real.

Finn liked to help his dad by giving each new gadget a "test run". To try them out he used them on a "School Spy" mission. Of course he had to sneak them out of the house without his dad knowing.

Finn's "School Spy" missions were a way to help other kids who found him on the internet. Finn could fix any kind of problem – he could sort out a bully, or get a mean teacher off your back. So many kids needed his help.

Finn put the gadgets into his school-bag. They would come in very handy on his latest mission.

Chapter 2
Time to Meet Tom

Finn arrived at a clearing in the woods and checked his watch. He was supposed to meet a new "School Spy" customer here at 8.00am. It wasn't even 7.30 and the clearing should have been empty. But it wasn't.

A scared-looking boy was sitting on a tree-stump with his arms folded tight across

his chest. He was dressed in a school
uniform at least two sizes too big. A pair of
very small glasses sat on his nose.

Finn pulled a notebook from his pocket, flicked it open, and read the name he had written in messy writing –

Tom Hibbert.

"Tom?" Finn asked, as he stepped out from behind a tree.

"Oh!" The boy jumped with fright and fell backwards off the stump.

The boy got to his feet as fast as he could. There were leaves all over his sweater and his glasses were stuck to his head at a funny angle.

"School Spy?" said the boy, and thrust his hand towards Finn.

"Yeah," Finn said. "My name's Finn Rock."

"Rock, Finn Rock?" asked the boy. "Like 'Bond, James Bond'?"

Finn smiled. "Nah, just Finn," he said.

"I'm Tom," said the boy.

Finn looked at him. He thought they might be in the same year at school, but Tom looked so shy that he seemed smaller. He was jumpy and he couldn't look Finn in the eye. Finn had seen other boys like him before and he knew it meant he was being bullied.

Finn remembered Tom's email:

Dear School Spy,

We've got a big problem with some big bullies.

They steal our money, our phones and even our bikes.

We can't take it any more. Can you help?

Tom Hibbert

"Have you got everything I asked for?" Finn asked.

Tom nodded. He took a bag off his back and tipped out everything inside.

"One school tie ... One jumper ... One blazer ... And one school-bag," he said.

Finn put on the clothes. They were almost the right size. And the school-bag had everything he needed in it.

"It's all there," Tom told him. "I ... um ... took them from the Lost Property cupboard yesterday. I had to guess what size you would be, School Spy."

"Call me Finn," said Finn. "Now, come on. I don't want to be late on my first day.

Chapter 3

School Spy Goes to School

Finn and Tom stood beside the school gates. It was still very early in the morning. The playground was empty, just how Finn liked it.

Tom was nervous. "Isn't this a bit risky?" he asked.

"Of course it is," said Finn. "That's what makes it fun." He grinned at Tom.

Tom looked like he could never understand how breaking into a school could ever be fun. Just then a big green BMW drove into the staff car park.

Tom pointed at the green car. "That's him," he said. "That's the Headmaster."

Finn opened the school-bag and pulled out a clip-board.

"Back in a second," he promised.

Finn walked up to the BMW as the school Headmaster got out of the car and looked at his reflection in the polished paint. He patted down his hair and then he saw Finn.

"Yes, boy?" he said.

Finn pretended to get a shock. He saw the Headmaster smile. He could tell the Headmaster wanted to make the pupils think that he had eyes in the back of his head.

"Morning, sir," Finn said. "Can you help me, please?"

The Headmaster turned round. "Of course. What can I do for you?"

"Can I have a copy of your signature?" Finn asked.

The Headmaster frowned and looked at Finn. "My signature?"

"Yes, sir, for my art project. It's all about different hand-writing and everyone says you have the neatest hand-writing in school."

The Headmaster looked pleased. "In that case ..." he said, and took the pen Finn held out for him.

The ink was still wet on the paper when Finn came back to Tom at the gates.

"Did he do it?" Tom asked. "Did he sign it?"

Finn smiled and unfolded the sheet of paper. Above the wet ink of the signature was a letter, typed on what looked like the school paper. Without knowing it, the Headmaster had just signed a letter from the school. The title read:

Pupil transfer letter.

Finn had tricked the Headmaster and it had been so easy. Wow, the School Spy was good!

"This letter will get me into your class, no problem," said Finn with a grin. "It works every time."

He grabbed Tom by the arm and pulled him towards the school doors. "Come on, Tom, you can show me to our class."

Chapter 4
Here Come the Bullies

Tom's teacher took one look at Finn's letter and told him he was welcome in her class.

"Sit here, School Spy," said Tom, and pointed to an empty seat next to his.

Finn shook his head, went to the row behind, and took a chair at the back of the class. "Sorry, Tom, I need to be where the problem is."

And it didn't take long for the problem to arrive.

First there was the sound of a pupil crying in the corridor outside.

"Here come the bullies," said Tom. He had his hand over his mouth so only Finn could hear him. "The big one is called Sacker and the small one is called Chan."

Then the two bullies walked into class. They hit the other pupils with rolled up books on the way past, and slammed heavy school-bags against the ones who ducked.

Chan was tall, thin and strong. His small dark eyes darted around the classroom, looking for a victim.

Sacker was huge. He stood behind his friend like a body-guard. Even his shadow was scary!

These boys were trouble. When they spotted Finn they glared at him. They sat in the seats beside him and snarled and spat. They thought they'd found a new victim!

Finn stayed calm. He'd met lots of bullies and these two were not as scary as they thought they were.

Half way into the first lesson, the bullies started.

"Hey, new boy!" hissed Sacker. "Have you got the answers to the test?"

Finn looked down at his sheet. The questions were easy – anyone could have done them if they had listened to the teacher. But Finn had left his sheet blank on purpose. He knew Sacker would ask.

"Maybe I do," he whispered back. "Why, haven't you? Oh, hang on – can you even spell your own name?"

The bully snarled, "Oh, you think you're a smarty pants, do you?"

"No," said Finn. "I'm just smart."

"Prove it," said Chan. "Write the answers on my sheet."

"I've got a better plan," Finn said.

As the bullies stared at him, Finn tried hard not to smile. It was almost too easy.

"Have you two losers got mobile phones?" he asked.

Sacker leaned close to Finn and waved a shiny smart-phone under his nose.

"iPhones," he said. "That good enough?"

Perfect, thought Finn. "It'll do," he said.

Finn passed the bullies a pen each. "Be good boys and write your numbers down for me."

"Why? Are you gonna ring us when we put you in hospital?" said Chan.

"No, stupid," said Finn. "I'm going to text you the teacher's answer sheet."

Chapter 5
The Bad Guys Fall For It

At last, Finn could test out one of his dad's new MI6 gadgets. He put his hand in his bag and pulled out a normal-looking Blackberry phone.

Only Finn knew it was anything but normal.

Finn's dad's top secret file said the phone was in fact a brand-new MI6 Hackberry. It worked like a normal mobile phone, but it also let you hack into any computer up to half a mile away. Only problem was it would only work once, because it was just a test model.

Luckily once was enough to get into the teacher's computer!

Finn pushed a few buttons to get into the lap-top's hard-drive, and in two seconds the teacher's answer sheet appeared on his screen. Two seconds more and the file was on the way to the bullies' iPhones.

BUZZ. BEEP!

"Hey, you're not half bad, for a swot," said Sacker.

"Better than you two losers," said Finn.

"Wanna prove that?" said Chan.

Finn smiled. "Yeah, why not?" he said.

Finn opened his bag and took out the second MI6 gadget – the coins. He slammed five of them on the desk in front of Sacker.

"Bet you five pounds I can beat you at anything!!"

"OK," said Sacker. "What will it be?"

"Stealing," said Finn. "You two against me. Whoever steals the most stuff from the school by the end of break wins this five quid."

When Sacker and Chan started to fight for the coins, Finn grinned. He loved it when bullies fell into one of his traps.

Chapter 6
Finn Gets Busy

Sacker and Chan were now on a mission of their own – to steal as much from the school as they could by the end of break. They had kept Finn's money, but Finn didn't mind. He had his own coin in his blazer pocket. And his was the one that mattered.

"I don't get it, School Spy," said Tom. "How does telling the bullies to steal stuff help us?"

Finn tapped his nose. "You'll see." He opened his bag again and took out two Blue-tooth ear-plugs. He put one in Tom's ear.

"What's this for?" Tom asked.

"You can be my eyes and ears," Finn told him.

Finn put the second plug in his own ear. Right away he could hear Tom breathing. The MI6 guys who made this kit were good!

"If you think I'm about to get caught, let me know," Finn said.

"Caught? I don't like the sound of that!" said Tom. "Caught where?"

"Follow me and you'll find out," said Finn.
He set off across the playground to the staff
offices on the other side.

Chapter 7
Time to Trick the Teachers

Finn left Tom hidden under a long coat hanging on a peg in the staff-room.

"I'll get caught," Tom said. "I just know it."

"No you won't," Finn promised. "Just keep watch and tell me if anyone comes."

Finn crept along the empty corridor. His watch told him he had just seven minutes to catch the bullies in his trap. He would have to act fast!

He looked at the signs that were stuck on the doors on both sides of the corridor.

School Secretary

Deputy Headmaster

Headmaster

Bingo! The Headmaster's office was the one he needed.

Finn pressed his ear to the Headmaster's door and listened. Nothing! He tried to open the door, but it was locked.

Finn knew there was a space above the rooms, under the floor above. He climbed onto a chair, reached up and opened a flap above him. Then he pulled himself up through the flap and into the dark above.

Aaaaa-choo!!

There was dust everywhere and Finn sneezed. He waited, held his breath and hoped no one had heard it. After a second, he let his breath out and began to crawl across to where there was another flap. He lifted it and looked down.

JACKPOT! Now he was above the Headmaster's office.

Finn dropped into the office without a sound and sat down in front of the Headmaster's lap-top. It was on.

Finn worked fast to hack into the Headmaster's programs. He had one called School Talk. Finn opened it.

"**Urgent!**" he typed. "**All teachers must go to the sports hall in five minutes.**

Any teacher who is late will be fired!

Pupils must go to the Library!"

Finn hit a button that said <Shout it out!> and smiled.

60 seconds later, Finn's message would be read out on the sound system in every class. The computer had stored the

Headmaster's voice so it would sound like it was him. All the teachers would panic as they rushed to get to the sports hall in time – none of them would dare to be late.

Finn hoped his trick would give Sacker and Chan plenty time to steal as much stuff as they could carry.

Finally, Finn hacked into the Deputy Headmaster's email from the Headmaster's lap-top. He sent an email to the Headmaster's Blackberry. It said:

"Fight at the school gates. Need help. NOW!"

Right then, Finn's Blue-tooth earplug burst into life.

"School Spy!" It was Tom. "Get out of there! The Headmaster's on his way."

Anyone else would have got scared, but not Finn. As he heard the Headmaster's key in the lock, he sat back in the chair, put his feet on the desk and waited.

The door never opened. Finn smiled as he heard the Headmaster's Blackberry beep to tell him he had a new e-mail. The Headmaster said a bad word, then Finn heard him stamp away.

Tom whispered through the earplug, "You're so lucky ..."

Chapter 8
Finn "Springs" Into Action

"Shouldn't we be running the other way?" said Tom as he and Finn ran after the Headmaster.

Finn shook his head. "We have to be at the school gates before the Headmaster if you want rid of Sacker and Chan."

"Who would have thought he would be so fast?" said Tom.

"I know – is there a short cut?" asked Finn.

"Not unless you can fly," said Tom. He pointed at a block of classrooms two floors high. "The gates are right behind there."

"OK," said Finn. "You can meet me there."

Finn didn't have wings but he did have his Secret Springs.

His dad's notes said the Springs were made from strong rubber. They would take you over a building two floors high with one jump.

Tom ran off towards the school gates. Finn took out the Springs and put them on his feet.

They looked stupid, but as soon as Finn tried a small jump, he saw how good they were. He shot three metres into the air. WOW! It was better than being a kangaroo!

With no time to spare, Finn bent his knees then jumped for real. This time, he shot up into the air even higher ... three metres ... four metres ... five metres. He jumped over the six metre high roof no problem and almost landed on the other side of the building. At the last minute he managed to land on the edge of the roof, with the school gates just metres below him.

Finn looked round and spotted the Headmaster stamping towards the gates. Sacker and Chan were on their way there too. Finn had to get between them – NOW!

Finn pulled his school-bag off his back, sat on it like a sledge and slid down the roof.

WHOOSH!!

He hoped the ground below was soft.

Chapter 9
The Bullies Get Busted

The Headmaster turned the corner and saw ... nothing.

No fight. No kids. No sign of the Deputy Head – just the new boy, covered in mud, grass and leaves.

"What's going on here?" he barked.

"Erm ..." Finn was trying to think of an answer when Sacker and Chan appeared.

"Oh no!" Sacker said as he spotted the Headmaster.

"You boys!" the Headmaster shouted. "Stay right where you are."

Sacker and Chan ran.

They didn't get very far.

Finn whipped out his MI6 coin and pressed the queen's head on it.

CLICK!

Finn's coin switched on the coins the bullies had taken from him before. They were not normal coins – they were very VERY strong electric magnets. MI6 wanted them to trap enemy spies by pinning them to cars and other metal.

The two bullies didn't stand a chance!

ZZZZINNNNG!!! Sacker crashed against a steel bus shelter.

CLAAANNNNGGGG!! Chan smashed into an iron bin.

"Aaaarrrggghh," the bullies both wailed.

Tom came round the corner. He stopped and stared.

Finn's coins had stuck the bullies to the metal better than super-strong superglue.

"Check their bags, sir," Finn said to the Headmaster. "I think you'll want to see what's inside."

"I'll get you back for this," hissed Sacker.

Chan wailed like a baby.

The Headmaster emptied the bags and gasped. They were full of iPods and lap-tops and other stuff from the school. It was all worth thousands of pounds!

"I'll have you put out of school for this," the Headmaster said. "You're both finished."

Tom and Finn high-fived.

"What about your five pounds?" Tom asked Finn as the Headmaster grabbed Sacker and Chan by their ears.

"Oh, I think I might get it back," said Finn. He winked and pressed the queen's head again.

RRRR-RIP!! The magnets pulled the other coins right through the bullies' pockets! Finn caught them as they flew back to him.

"My work here is done!" said Finn.

Tom smiled. "Thanks, Secret Spy."

"Don't thank me," said Finn. "Thank MI6!"